5 . 62
3
p. 130
. 134
. 145
. 150

THE SAVAGE AND BEAUTIFUL COUNTRY